level I

NOTE SPELLER

by JAMES BASTIEN

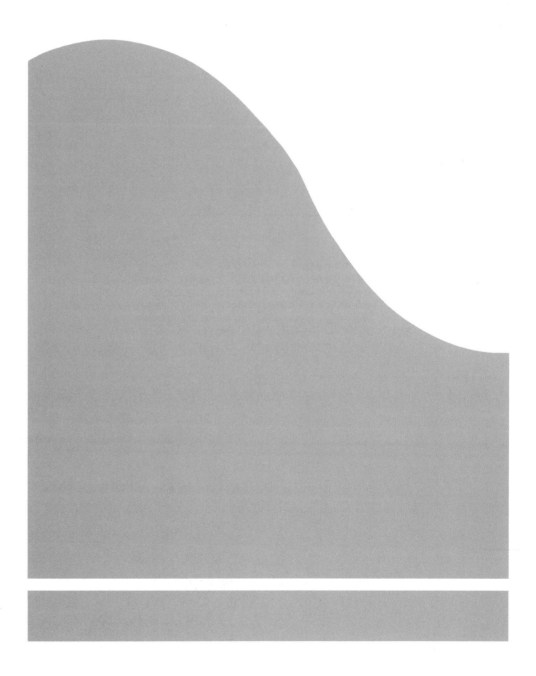

KJOS WEST • Neil A. Kjos Music Company, Publisher • San Diego, California

PREFACE

The "NOTE SPELLER" is designed to introduce basic information about the staff, notes and rests, accidentals, and leger line notes. It can be used for both private and group instruction, and for both piano and organ lessons.

In addition to the written lessons in this book, the student should play all examples on the keyboard. By playing all the notes, the student will develop the correct sense of location on the keyboard. Also, the BASTIEN "MUSIC FLASHCARDS" should be used in conjunction with the "NOTE SPELLER" to provide sufficient home drill.

The "NOTE SPELLER" provides elementary information to reinforce the materials in Level One of the BASTIEN PIANO LIBRARY. It can also be used with any other piano course.

ISBN 0-8497-5019-9

CONTENTS

LESSON 1. Lines and Spaces on the Staff

A music STAFF has five LINES and four SPACES. The lines and spaces are numbered from the bottom to the top.

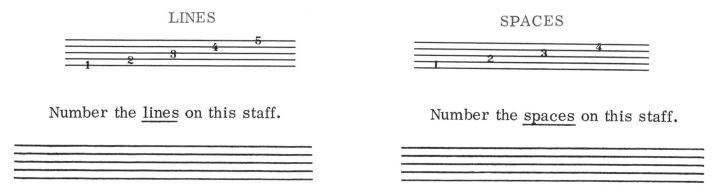

Number the <u>lines</u> on this staff.

Number the <u>spaces</u> on this staff.

FIVE LINE NOTES and FOUR SPACE NOTES may be written on the staff.

Line and space notes are written on these staffs. Write <u>L</u> on the blanks below the line notes and <u>S</u> on the blanks below the space notes.

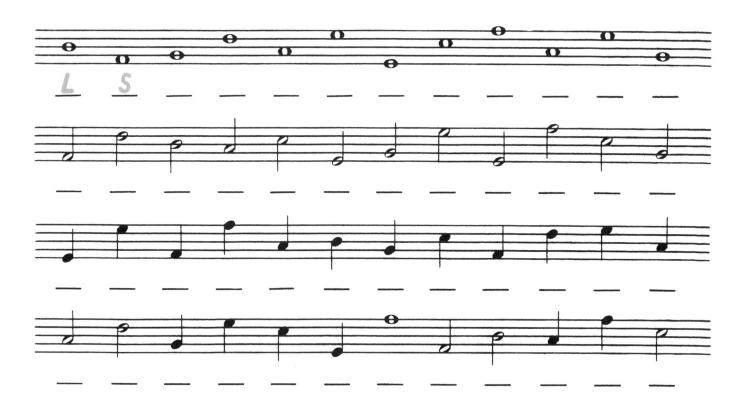

LESSON 2. Line and Space Note Numbers

Write the number of each <u>line</u> note on this staff.   Remember to count up from the bottom to the top.

Draw notes on the <u>lines</u> of the staff indicated by the numbers below.   Use whole notes.

3   1   5   4   2   3   5   1   3   2   4   1

2   5   1   3   4   1   5   3   2   4   2   5

Write the number of each <u>space</u> note on this staff.

Draw notes in the <u>spaces</u> of the staff indicated by the numbers below.   Use whole notes.

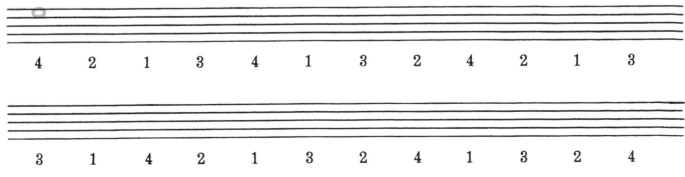

4   2   1   3   4   1   3   2   4   2   1   3

3   1   4   2   1   3   2   4   1   3   2   4

WP20

LESSON 3. Line and Space Note Numbers (combined)

Line and space notes are written on these staffs. Under each note write the number and either L for line note or S for space note.

Draw notes on the lines or in the spaces indicated. Use whole notes.

1L	4S	3L	2S	5L	1S	2L	4L	3S

3L	2S	4L	4S	2L	1S	4S	5L	1L

2S	4L	3S	2L	5L	3L	1S	4S	1L

LESSON 4. Drawing Stems on Notes

Here are three kinds of notes:

WHOLE NOTE   HALF NOTE   QUARTER NOTE

With the exception of the whole note, all notes have stems. The stem is on the <u>right</u> side of a note when the stem is up.

Draw <u>up</u> stems on these note heads.

The stem is on the <u>left</u> side of a note when the stem is down.

Draw <u>down</u> stems on these note heads.

Notes on or above the middle line have down stems.
Notes below the middle line have up stems.

DOWN STEMS   UP STEMS

Draw stems on these note heads.

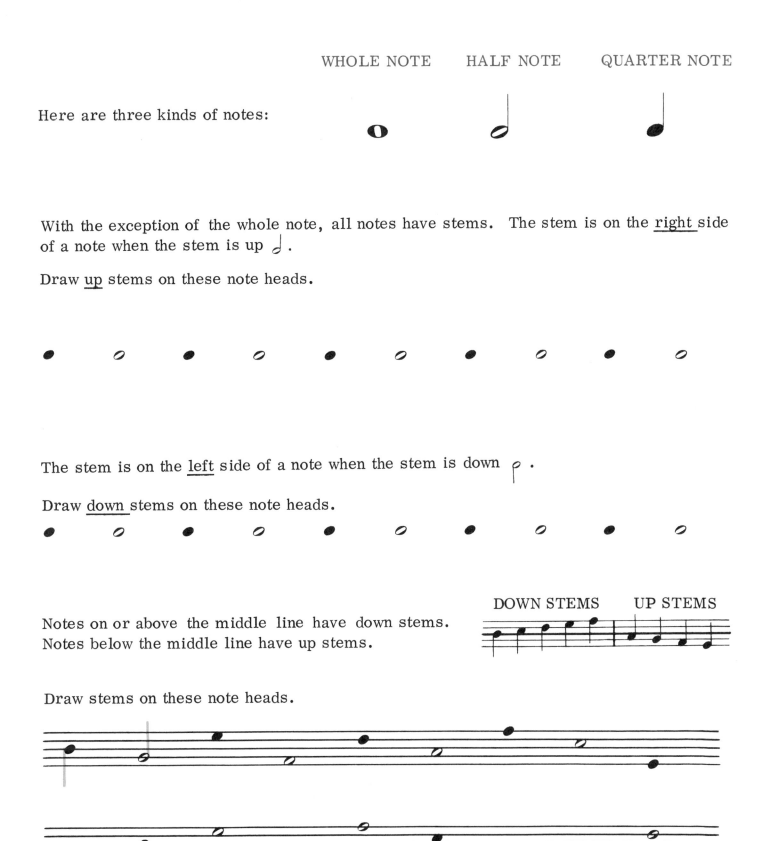

WP20

LESSON 5. Notes and Rests

TABLE OF NOTES AND RESTS

NOTES		RESTS	
o	Whole Note	▬	Whole Rest
♩	Half Note	▬	Half Rest
♩	Quarter Note	𝄽	Quarter Rest

Using these abbreviations, identify the following notes and rests:

W for Whole Note or Whole Rest
H for Half Note or Half Rest
Q for Quarter Note or Quarter Rest

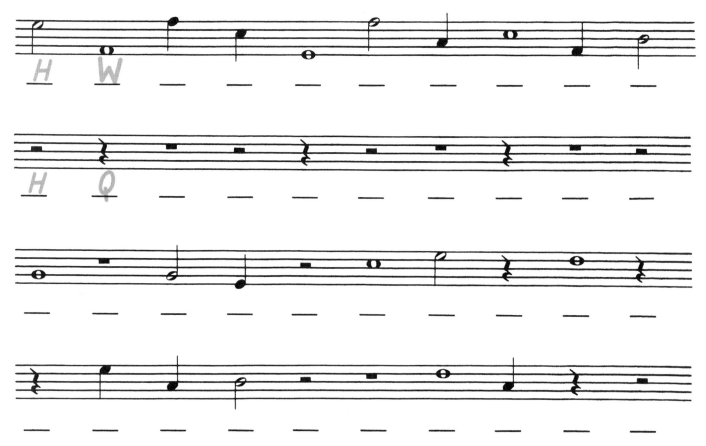

LESSON 6. Notes and Rests, continued

Draw Whole Rests on this staff. A Whole Rest "hangs" down from the <u>fourth</u> line.

Draw Half Rests on this staff. A Half Rest "sits" up on the <u>third</u> line. A Half Rest looks like a hat.

Draw Quarter Rests on this staff.

Draw the notes or rests indicated. Remember to draw the up or down stems correctly.

Q note 3rd line	H rest	W note 4th space	Q rest	H note 1st space	Q note 4th space	W rest

H note 4th line	W rest	Q rest	Q note 2nd line	H note 2nd space	H rest	W note 5th line

H rest	H note 3rd space	Q note 1st line	W note 3rd line	Q rest	W rest	H note 4th space

LESSON 7. The Grand Staff

Piano music is written on the GRAND STAFF. The Grand Staff has two sets of lines and spaces.

The upper part of the Grand Staff is called the Treble Staff. A Treble Clef or G Clef sign is used at the beginning of this staff. Middle to high notes are written on this staff.

Draw some Treble Clef signs.

The lower part of the Grand Staff is called the Bass Staff. A Bass Clef or F Clef sign is used at the beginning of this staff. Middle to low notes are written on this staff.

Draw some Bass Clef signs.

The Treble and Bass Staffs are joined together by a BRACE and a BAR LINE to form the GRAND STAFF.

BAR LINE
GRAND STAFF
BRACE →

Make Grand Staffs by adding clef signs, braces and bar lines.

WP20

LESSON 8. Line and Space Names on the Grand Staff

The MUSICAL ALPHABET has <u>seven</u> letters: A B C D E F G.

Write the Musical Alphabet <u>forward</u>.   *A* ___ ___ ___ ___ ___ ___

Write the Musical Alphabet <u>backward</u>.   ___ ___ ___ ___ ___ ___ *G*

Circle every other letter in the Musical Alphabet.   These are alphabet skips.

Ⓐ B Ⓒ D E F G A B C D E F G A B C D E F G A B C

Circle every other letter in this row.

Ⓖ A B C D E F G A B C D E F G A B C D E F

The <u>lines</u> on the Grand Staff are arranged by <u>alphabet</u> <u>skips</u>.
The line names are: G B D F A C E G B D F.

Write the letter names of the line on this Grand Staff.*

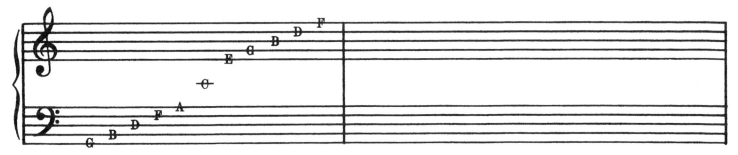

Circle every other letter in this row.

Ⓕ G A B C D E F G A B C D E F G A B C D E F G

The <u>spaces</u> on the Grand Staff are arranged by <u>alphabet</u> <u>skips</u>.
The space names are: F A C E G B D F A C E G.

Write the letter names of the spaces on this Grand Staff.*

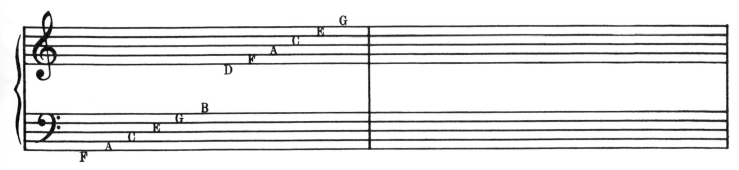

*TEACHER: Have the student write the line and space names in this manner
    in his BASTIEN "MUSIC NOTEBOOK."

WP20

LESSON 9. Treble Clef Line Notes

The letter names of the Treble Clef line notes form alphabet skips: E G B D F.*

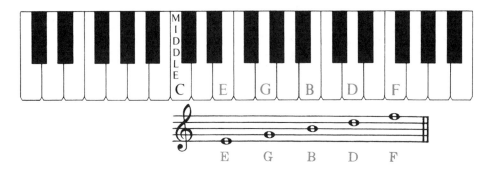

Write the correct letter name under each Treble Clef line note.

Write the letter names of these line notes. The letter names spell words.

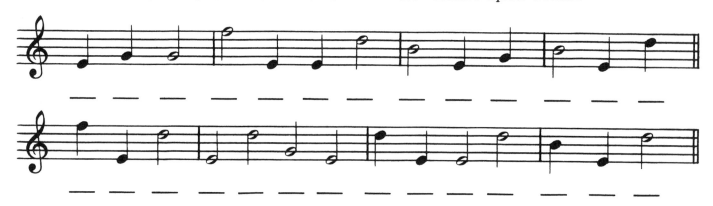

Draw a line note above each letter name. Use half notes. Remember to draw the up or down stems correctly. (See page 7 again.)

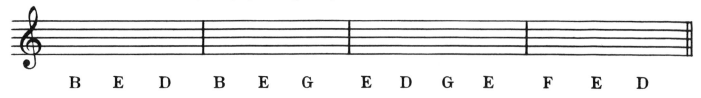

B   E   D   B   E   G   E   D   G   E   F   E   D

TEACHER: Have the student drill on these notes using his BASTIEN "MUSIC FLASHCARDS."

WP20

LESSON 10. Treble Clef Space Notes

The letter names of the Treble Clef space notes form alphabet skips which spell the word:
F A C E.*

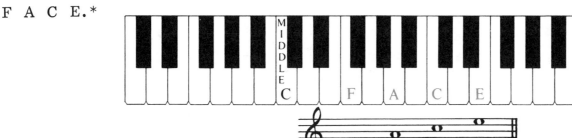

Write the correct letter name under each Treble Clef space note.

Write the letter names of these space notes. The letter names spell words.

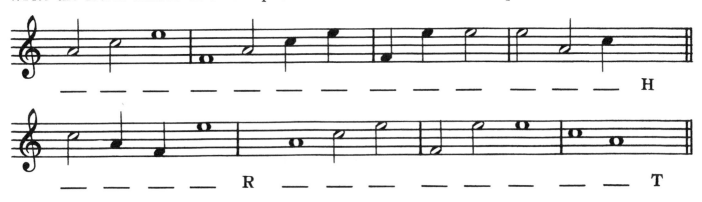

Draw a space note above each letter name. Use quarter notes (fill in the notes). Remember to draw the up or down stems correctly.

F E E   C A F E   A C E   F A C E

* *TEACHER: Have the student drill on these notes using his BASTIEN "MUSIC FLASHCARDS."*

LESSON 11. Treble Clef Line and Space Notes (combined)

Write the letter names of these Treble Clef notes.   The letter names spell words.

Draw a note above each letter name. Use half notes.

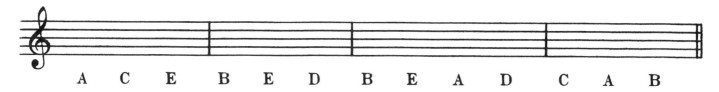

A   C   E   B   E   D   B   E   A   D   C   A   B

Draw the exact Treble Clef notes described.

Use half notes.

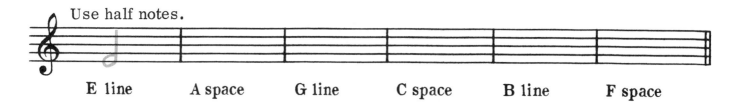

E line   A space   G line   C space   B line   F space

Use quarter notes.

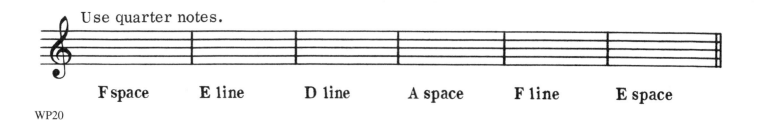

F space   E line   D line   A space   F line   E space

LESSON 12. Treble Clef Notes Outside the Staff

Notes may be written outside the staff. Extra lines added above and below the staff are called LEGER LINES.

Here are three Treble Clef notes that are placed outside the staff. Middle C is written on a leger line below the Treble Staff. D is written in the space below the Treble Staff. G is written in the space above the Treble Staff.*

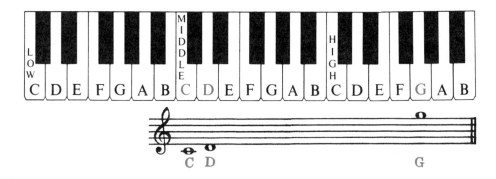

Write the letter names of these Treble Clef notes.

Draw the exact Treble Clef notes described.

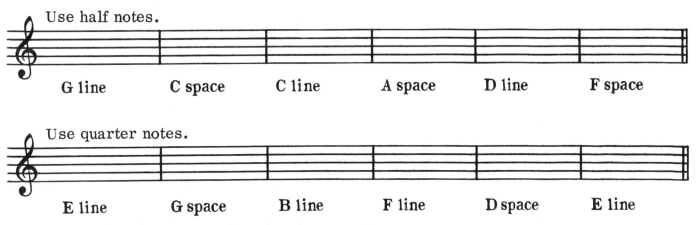

Use half notes.

| G line | C space | C line | A space | D line | F space |

Use quarter notes.

| E line | G space | B line | F line | D space | E line |

TEACHER: Have the students include these three notes for drill on all the Treble Clef notes using his BASTIEN "MUSIC FLASHCARDS."

LESSON 13. Bass Clef Line Notes

The letter names of the Bass Clef line notes form alphabet skips: G B D F A.*

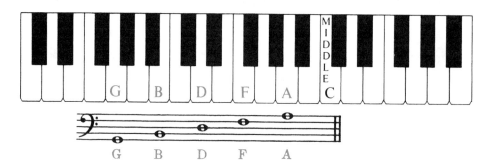

Write the correct letter name under each Bass Clef line note.

Write the letter names of these line notes. The letter names spell words.

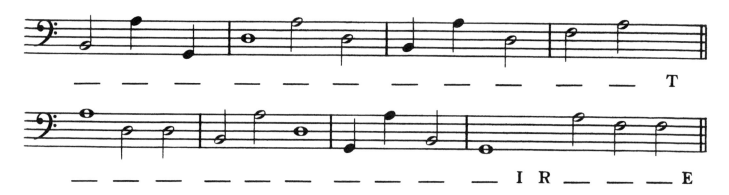

Draw a line note above each letter name. Use half notes. Remember to draw the up or down stems correctly.

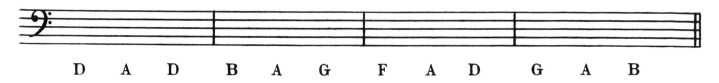

D   A   D   B   A   G   F   A   D   G   A   B

TEACHER: Have the student drill on these notes using his BASTIEN "MUSIC FLASHCARDS."

LESSON 14. Bass Clef Space Notes

The letter names of the Bass Clef space notes form alphabet skips: A C E G.*

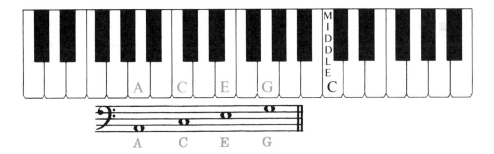

Write the correct letter name under each Bass Clef space note.

Write the letter names of these space notes. The letter names spell words.

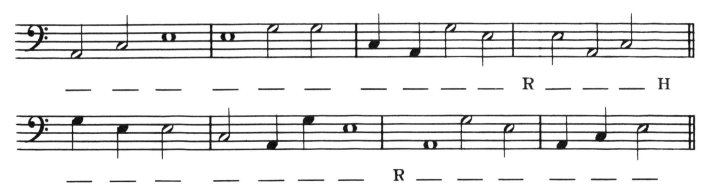

Draw a space note above each letter name. Use quarter notes. Remember to draw the up or down stems correctly.

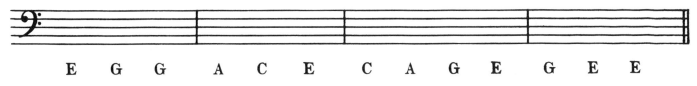

E G G   A C E   C A G   E G E E

*TEACHER: *Have the student drill on these notes using his BASTIEN "MUSIC FLASHCARDS."*

LESSON 15. Bass Clef Line and Space Notes (combined)

Write the letter names of these Bass Clef notes.   The letter names spell words.

Draw a note above each letter name. Use half notes.

B   E   D   F   A   C   E   D   E   A   F   B   E   A   D

Draw the exact Bass Clef notes described.

Use half notes.

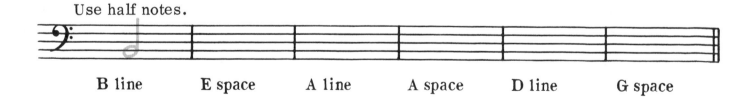

B line   E space   A line   A space   D line   G space

Use quarter notes.

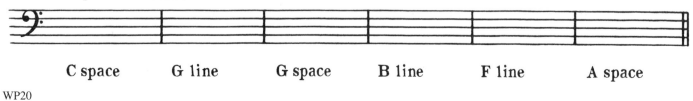

C space   G line   G space   B line   F line   A space

LESSON 16. Bass Clef Notes Outside the Staff

Here are three Bass Clef notes that are placed outside the staff. F is written in the space below the Bass Staff. B is written in the space above the Bass Staff. Middle C is written on a leger line above the Bass Staff.

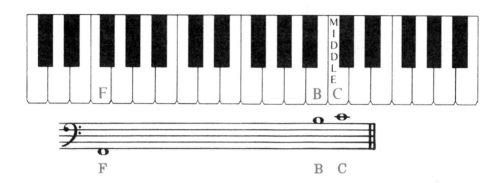

Write the letter names of these Bass Clef notes.

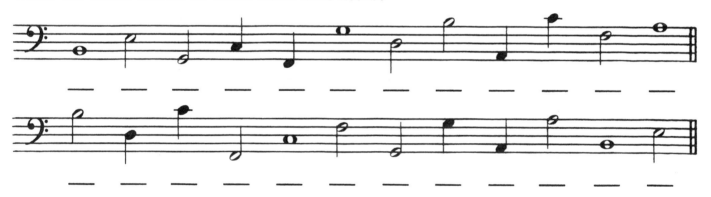

Draw the exact Bass Clef notes described.

Use half notes.

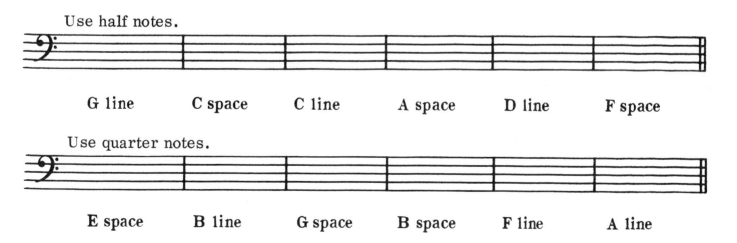

| G line | C space | C line | A space | D line | F space |

Use quarter notes.

| E space | B line | G space | B space | F line | A line |

* *TEACHER: Have the student include these three notes for drill on all the Bass Clef notes using his BASTIEN "MUSIC FLASHCARDS."*

20

LESSON 17. Notes on the Grand Staff

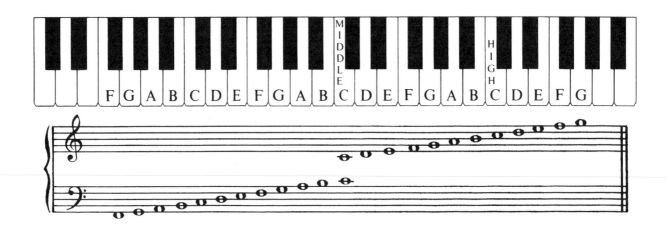

Write the letter names of these notes. Look carefully to see if the notes are in the Treble Clef or Bass Clef.   The letter names spell words.

* *TEACHER: Have the student drill on all the notes of both clefs shown above using his BASTIEN "MUSIC FLASHCARDS."*

LESSON 18. Notes on the Grand Staff, continued

Write the letter names of these notes.   The letter names spell words.

— — O R — — — — — K — — M — N T

— — — — — — — — — — — N — Y

Draw a note above each letter name in either the Treble Clef or the Bass Clef.

Use half notes.

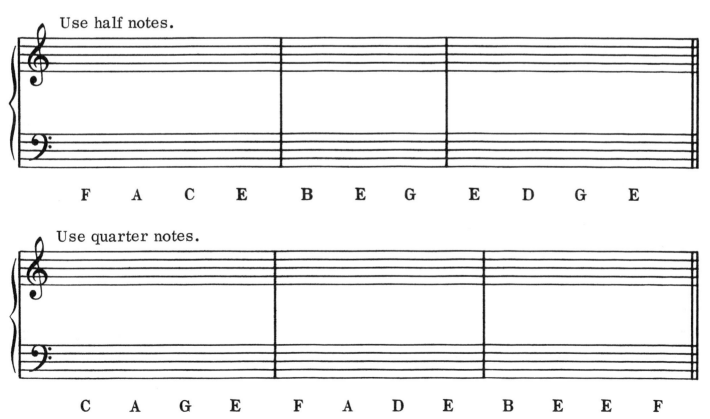

F A C E   B E G   E D G E

Use quarter notes.

C A G E   F A D E   B E E F

LESSON 19. Specific Notes on the Grand Staff

Draw the exact notes described.   T.C. means Treble Clef.   B.C. means Bass Clef.

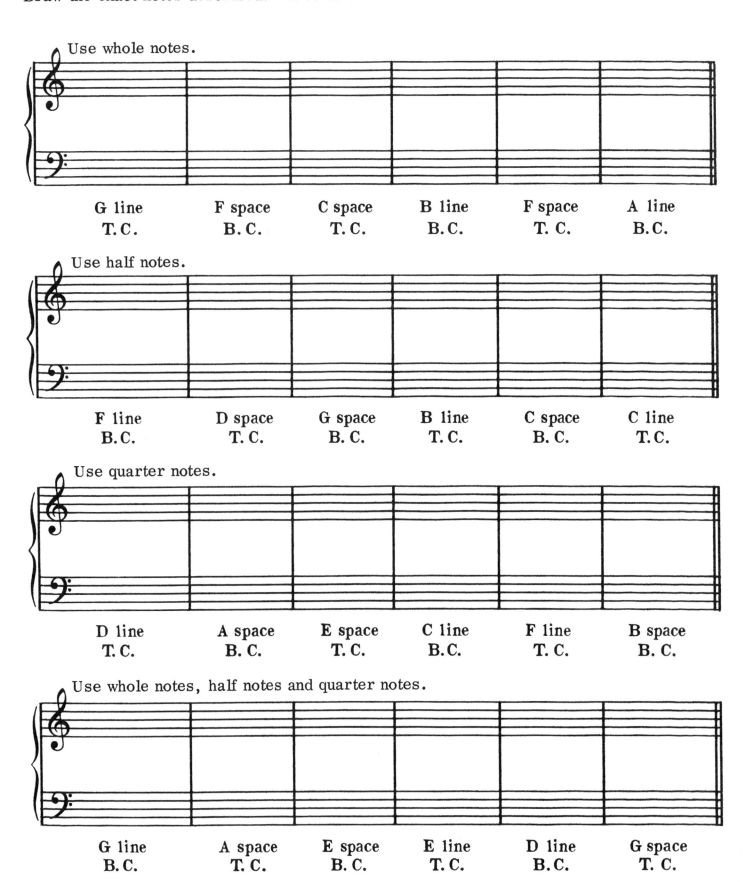

Use whole notes.

G line	F space	C space	B line	F space	A line
T.C.	B.C.	T.C.	B.C.	T.C.	B.C.

Use half notes.

F line	D space	G space	B line	C space	C line
B.C.	T.C.	B.C.	T.C.	B.C.	T.C.

Use quarter notes.

D line	A space	E space	C line	F line	B space
T.C.	B.C.	T.C.	B.C.	T.C.	B.C.

Use whole notes, half notes and quarter notes.

G line	A space	E space	E line	D line	G space
B.C.	T.C.	B.C.	T.C.	B.C.	T.C.

LESSON 20. Specific Notes on the Grand Staff, continued

Line and space notes with the <u>same</u> letter name appear in different locations in the Treble and Bass Clefs. Notice that line notes in the Treble Clef are placed one line <u>higher</u> than those with the same name in the Bass Clef. Space notes in the Treble Clef are placed one space <u>higher</u> than those with the same name in the Bass Clef.

Play these notes in their correct location on the keyboard.

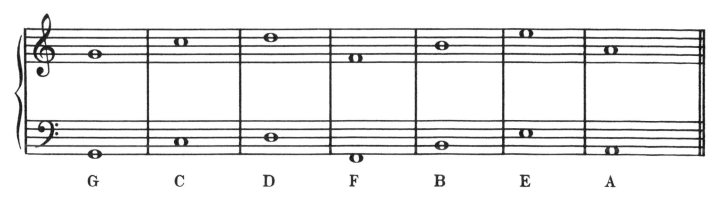

G   C   D   F   B   E   A

Draw two notes for each letter given. Either draw one line note on each staff or one space note on each staff. Use half notes.

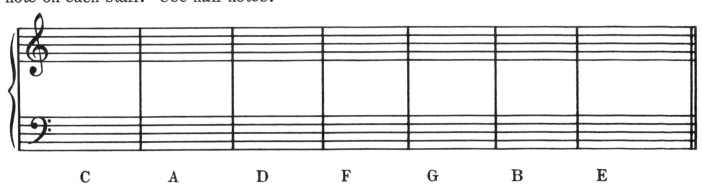

C   A   D   F   G   B   E

Draw either three or four notes for each letter given. Use whole notes.

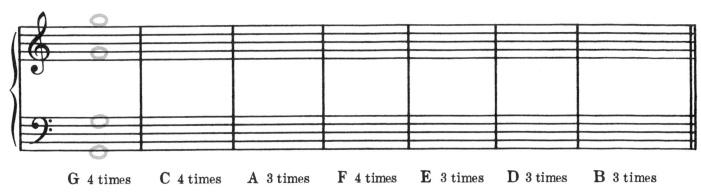

G 4 times   C 4 times   A 3 times   F 4 times   E 3 times   D 3 times   B 3 times

LESSON 21. Sharps, Flats and Naturals

The SHARP sign forms a square on a line   #   or in a space   #   .

Draw five sharps. First draw two lines <u>down.</u> Next draw two lines <u>across.</u>

Write the letter names under these sharps. Look carefully to see if the square part of the sharp is on a line or in a space.

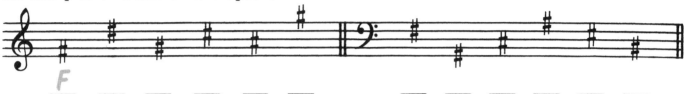

F _ _ _ _ _ _ _ _ _

The FLAT sign forms a rounded part on a line ♭ or in a space ♭ .

Draw five flats. First draw a <u>straight</u> line. Next draw a <u>curved</u> line.

Write the letter names under these flats. Look carefully to see if the rounded part of the flat is on a line or in a space.

B _ _ _ _ _ _ _ _ _

The NATURAL sign forms a square on a line ♮ or in a space ♮ .

Draw five naturals. First draw an L. Next draw an upside down L.

Write the letter names under these naturals. Look carefully to see if the square part of the natural is on a line or in a space.

D _ _ _ _ _ _ _ _

LESSON 22. Sharps, Flats and Naturals, continued

Sharps, flats and natural signs written <u>before</u> notes are called ACCIDENTALS.

A sharp before a note means to play the next key to the <u>right.</u> Sharps go UP.

Draw a sharp before each note. Write the letter name of each note on the blank below. The letter names spell words.

A flat before a note means to play the next key to the <u>left.</u> Flats go DOWN.

Draw a flat before each note. Write the letter name of each note on the blank below. The letter names spell words.

A natural before a note cancels a sharp or flat. It means to play the natural key (white key).

Draw a natural before the second note in each measure. Write the letter name of the note on the blank below.

Write the letter names under these accidentals. The letter names spell words.

WP20

LESSON 23. Leger Line and Space Notes

LEGER LINES are short lines that are added above and below the staff. The staff is extended (stretched) by adding these lines. Notes are written on these lines and spaces.

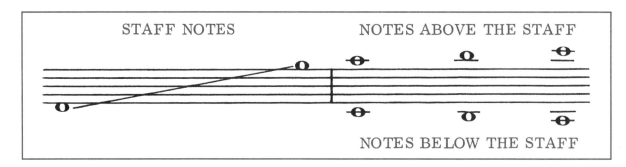

Three notes above the Bass Staff are C D E:*

Write the letter names of these notes. The letter names spell words.

Three notes below the Treble Staff are C B A:*

Write the letter names of these notes. The letter names spell words.

Write the letter names of these <u>inner</u> leger line and space notes.

*TEACHER: Have the student drill on these notes using his BASTIEN "MUSIC FLASHCARDS."

LESSON 24. Leger Line and Space Notes, continued

Three notes above the Treble Staff are A B C:*

Write the letter names of these notes.   The letter names spell words.

Three notes below the Bass Staff are E D C:*

Write the letter names of these notes.   The letter names spell words.

Write the letter names of these <u>outer</u> leger line and space notes.

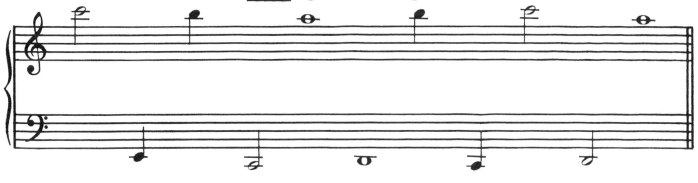

Write the letter names of these leger line and space notes.

TEACHER: Have the student drill on these notes using his BASTIEN "MUSIC FLASHCARDS."

LESSON 25. Notes Played Together

When one note is above another, both notes are played together at the <u>same</u> time.

Write the letter names of both notes.

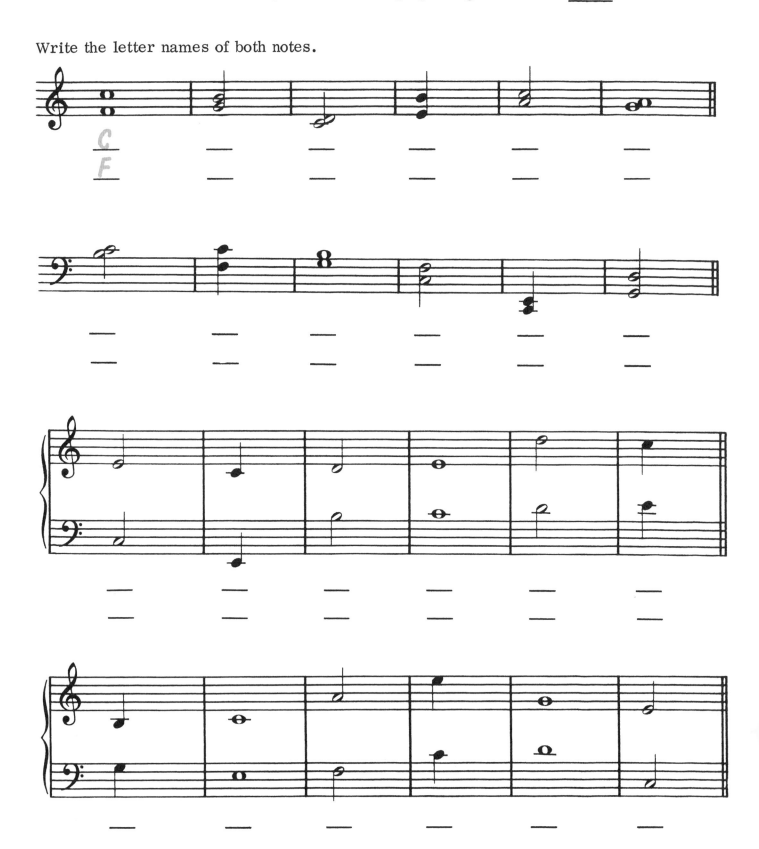

LESSON 26. Notes Played Together, continued

Write the letter names of these notes.

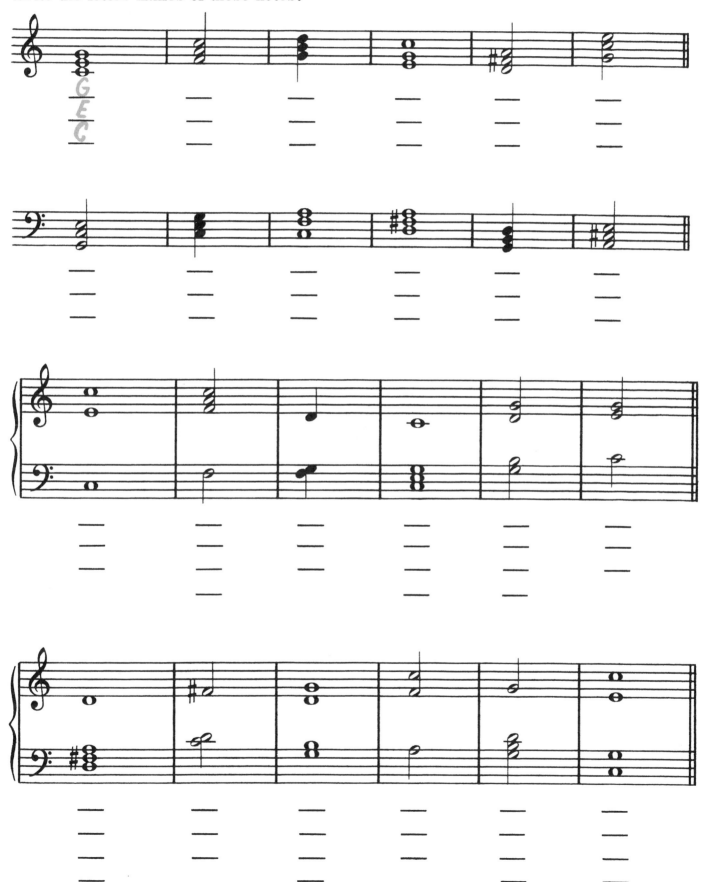

LESSON 27. Specific Note Names

Write the letter names of these notes.

Draw the exact notes described. Some of them are leger line and space notes.

Use half notes.

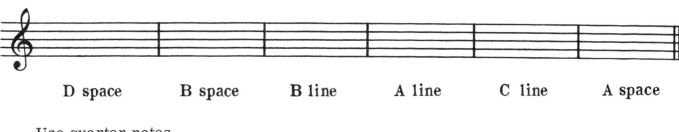

| D space | B space | B line | A line | C line | A space |

Use quarter notes.

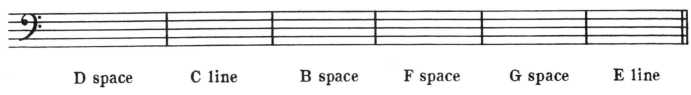

| D space | C line | B space | F space | G space | E line |

LESSON 28. Review

1. Under each note write the number and either L for line note or S for space note.

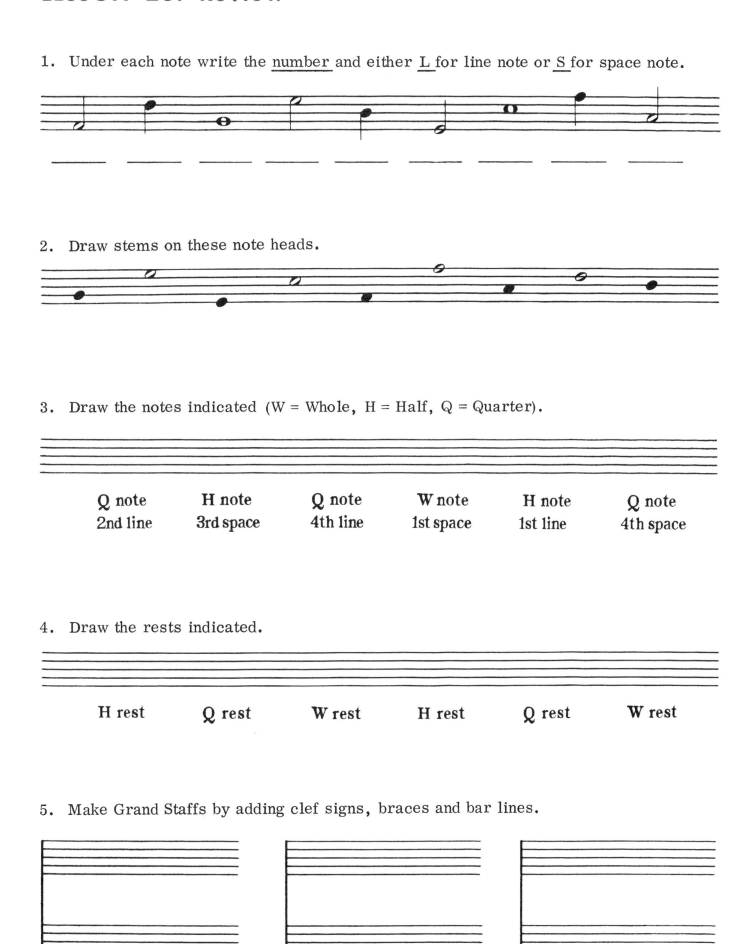

2. Draw stems on these note heads.

3. Draw the notes indicated (W = Whole, H = Half, Q = Quarter).

Q note	H note	Q note	W note	H note	Q note
2nd line	3rd space	4th line	1st space	1st line	4th space

4. Draw the rests indicated.

H rest	Q rest	W rest	H rest	Q rest	W rest

5. Make Grand Staffs by adding clef signs, braces and bar lines.

WP20

Review, continued

6. Draw two notes for each letter given. Either draw one line note on each staff or one space note on each staff. Use quarter notes.

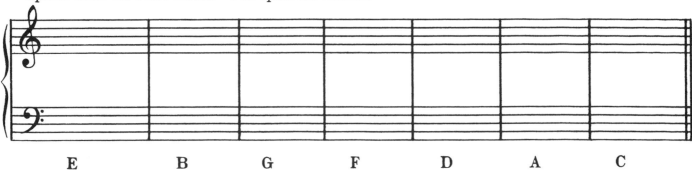

E   B   G   F   D   A   C

7. Write the letter names of these accidentals.

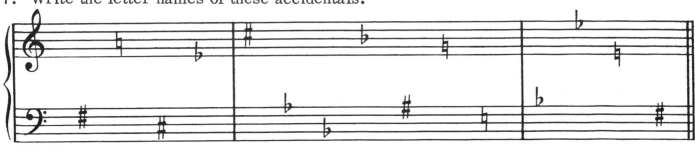

8. Write the letter names of these notes.

9. Write the letter names of these notes.

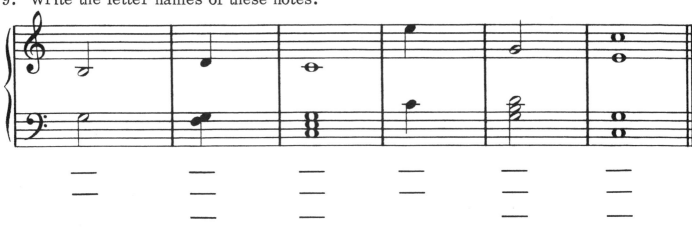